The
SECRET THOUGHTS of
WOMEN
&
MEN

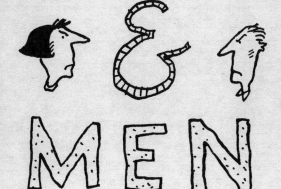

*Steven Appleby*

GQ EDITION

For Michael VerMeulen

First published in Great Britain 1996

This edition published 1996

Bloomsbury Publishing PLC
38 Soho Square, London W1V 5DF

A CIP catalogue record for this book
is available from the British Library

ISBN 0 7475 3230 3

Printed in Great Britain by
Cox & Wyman Limited, Reading

# The
# SECRET
# THOUGHTS
# of
# WOMEN

MANY THANKS TO:

Abigail; Gill; Janny;
Jean; Jessamy; Karen;
Kate; Linda; Liz;
Lorna; Mary; Nicola;
Noni; Rachel; Ros &
Sophie.

W/up liquid.   Persil/Cond

CHOC!   toilet cleaner   Hoover

Sugar   tampons   bird

Bread   nappies   Bathsponge   cat

butter   flour.   (cat

crisps

veg:   cereals

carrots, peas   baby food

potatoes/new

leeks

tomatoes   arsenic

lettuce   sharp knives

S. onions

cucumber   polythene sheeting.

spade

...itioner.

bags

. seed

food

litter?)

CHAMPAGNE!!
chocolate.

N.B.
recycle
- newspapers
- jars
- tins etc.
- ~~husband~~

→ N.B. - Grass seed &
assorted plants.

MAKE ~~✗✗✗✗~~ ✗
✗ HAIR APPOINTMENT!

Get HOLIDAY BROCHURES!!

new suite.    - passport.
fast car.     - travellers'
clothes / suitcase(s)   cheques
Bikini        toothbrush.

By the time I'm 30 I'll be married with a couple of kids.

AGE 20

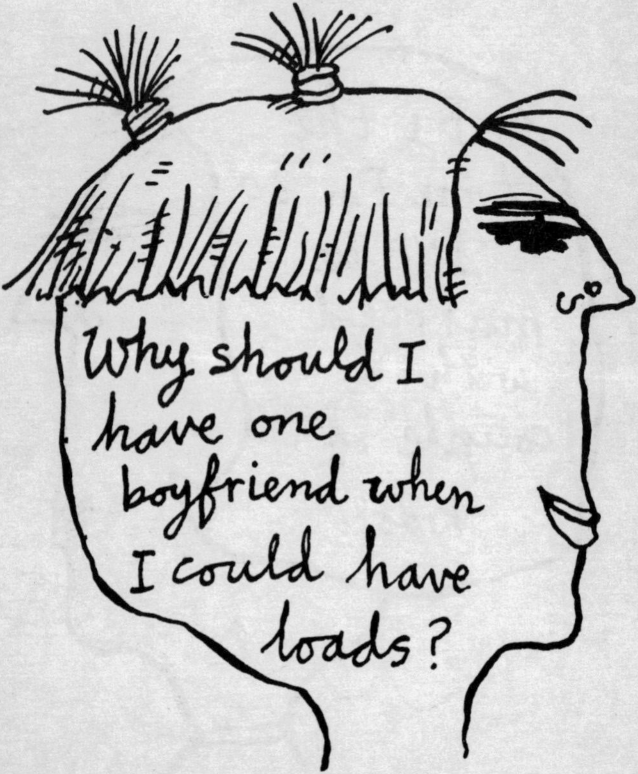

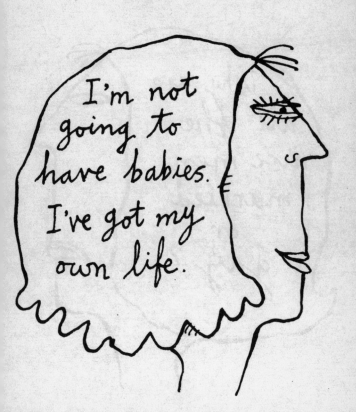

Perhaps I'll have kids... in a year or so!

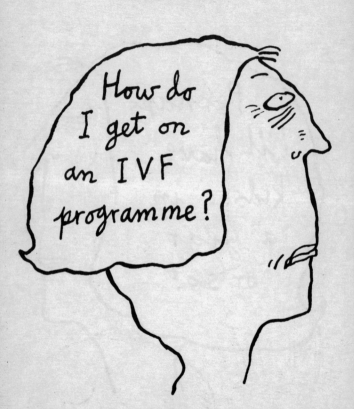

How do I get on an IVF programme?

Your new baby? How GORGEOUS... SWEET... DARLING...
My God, he looks like a monkey!

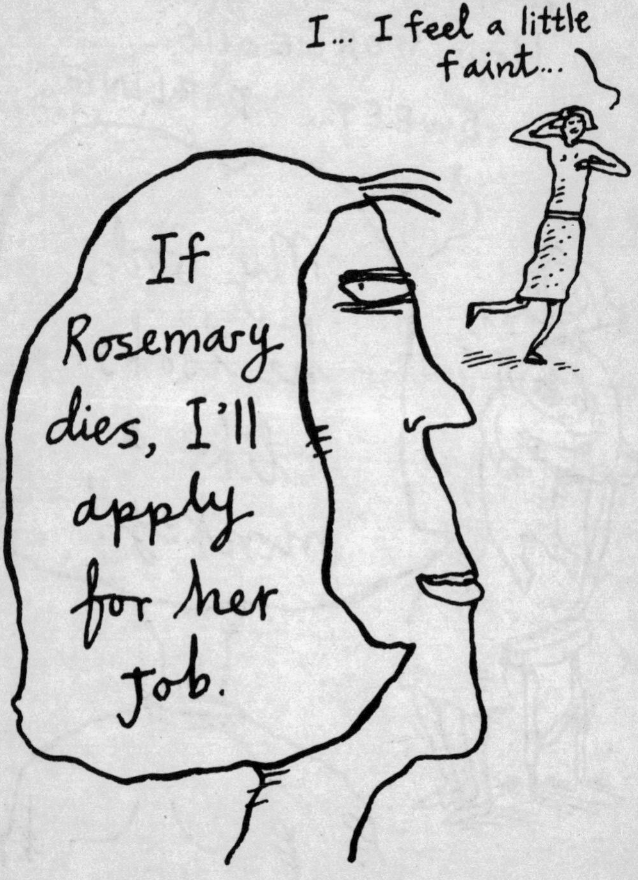
I... I feel a little faint...
If Rosemary dies, I'll apply for her job.

As soon as someone leaves the room I'm going to talk about them.
The loo? Top of the stairs on the right.

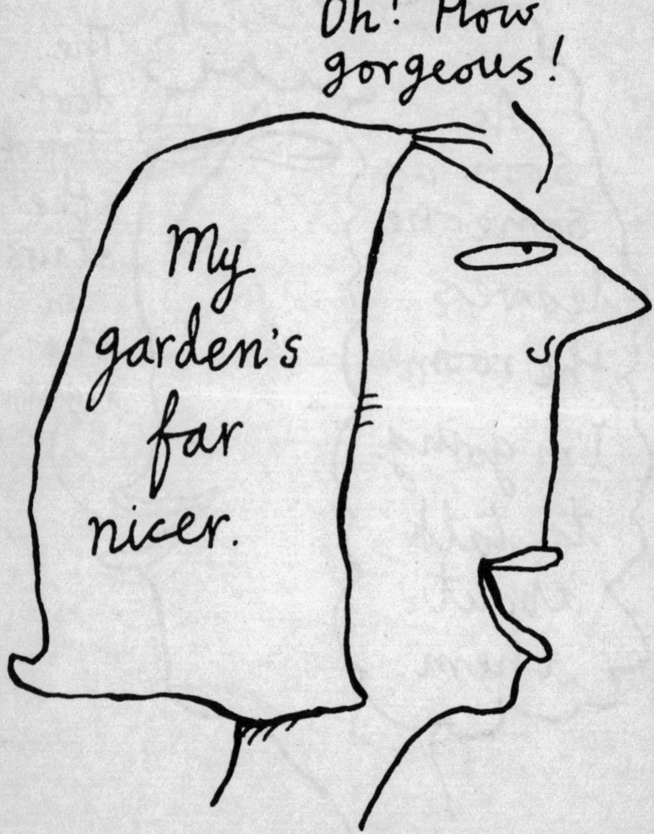
Oh! How gorgeous!
My garden's far nicer.

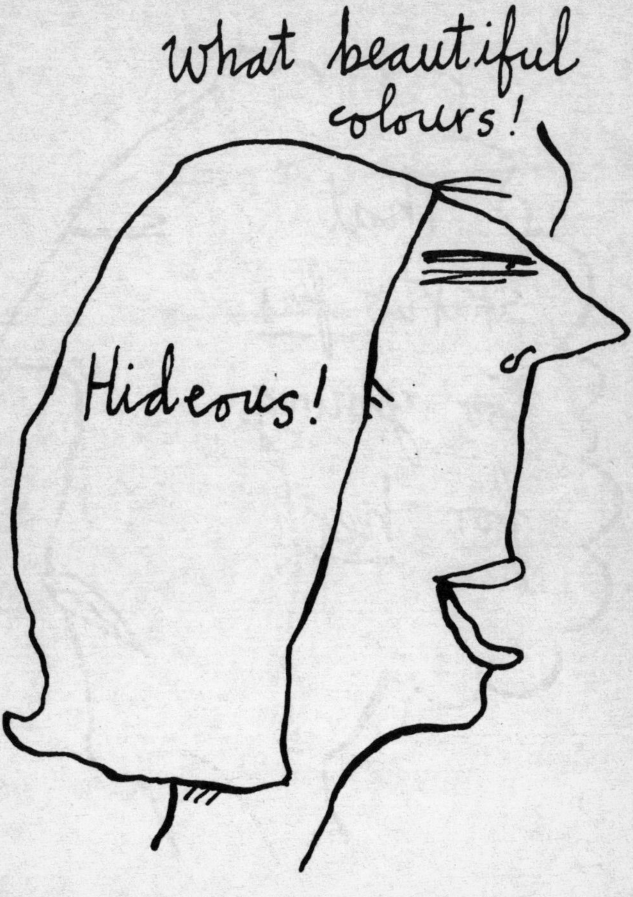
What beautiful colours!
Hideous!

And she's
wearing so
much make-up
she looks like
a transvestite.

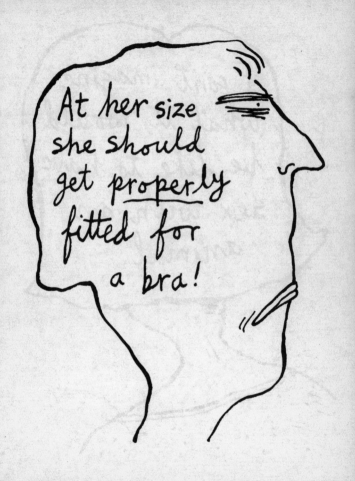

I can't imagine what it would be like to have sex with an animal...

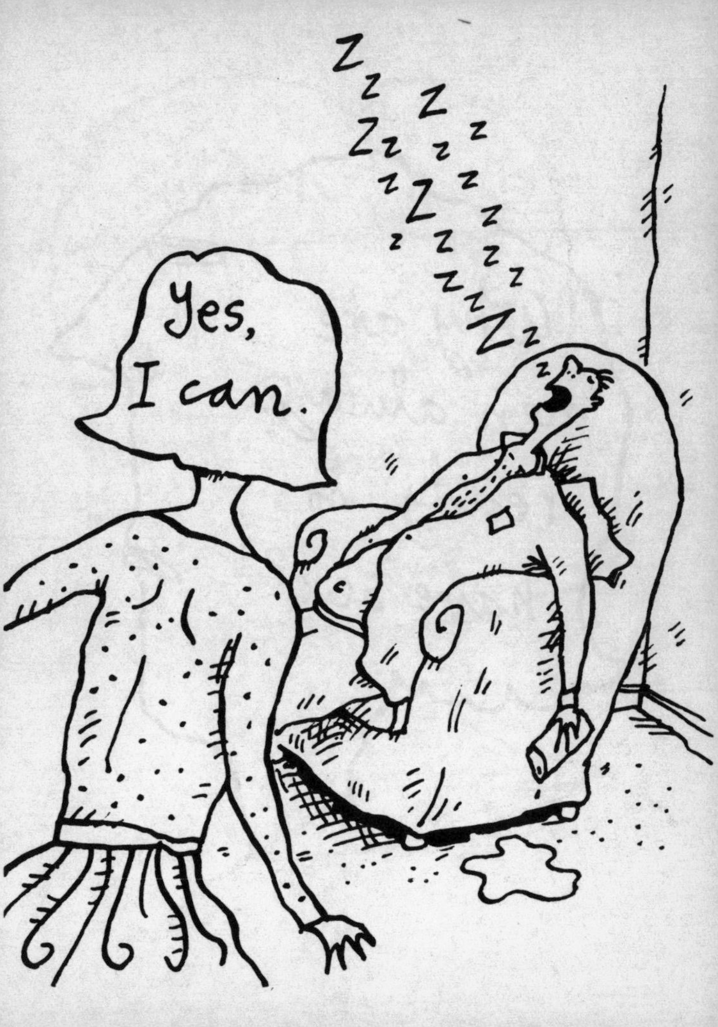
Yes, I can.

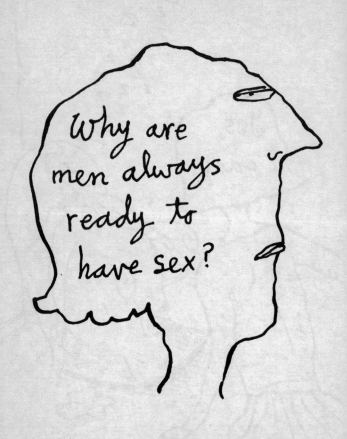

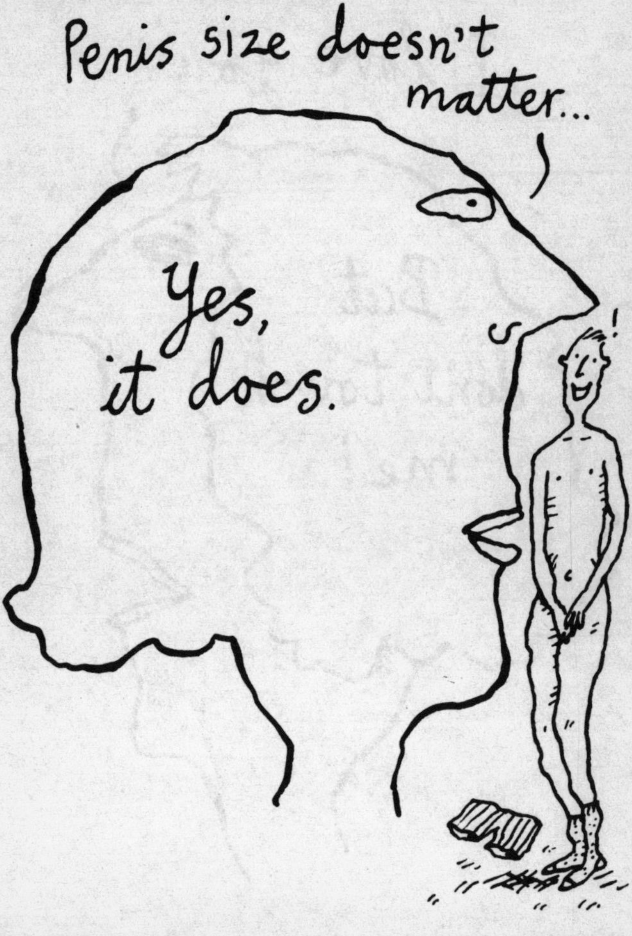
Penis size doesn't matter...
Yes, it does.
!

I've got a headache.

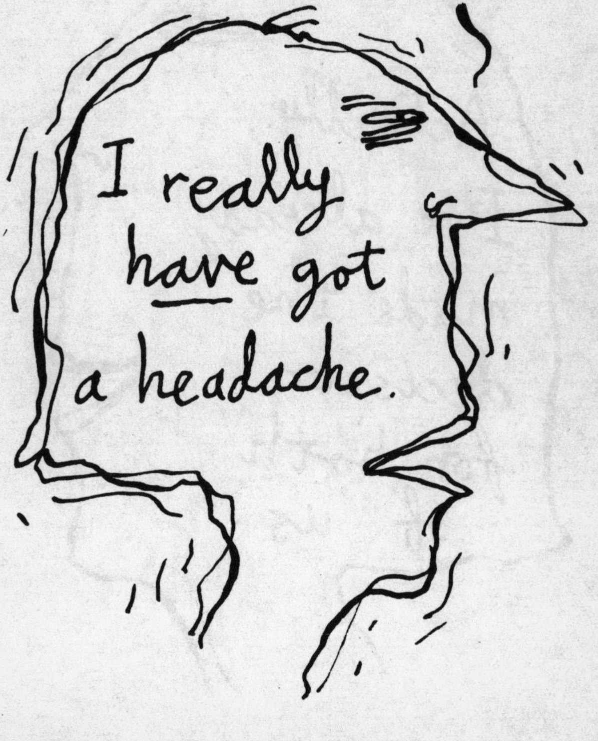

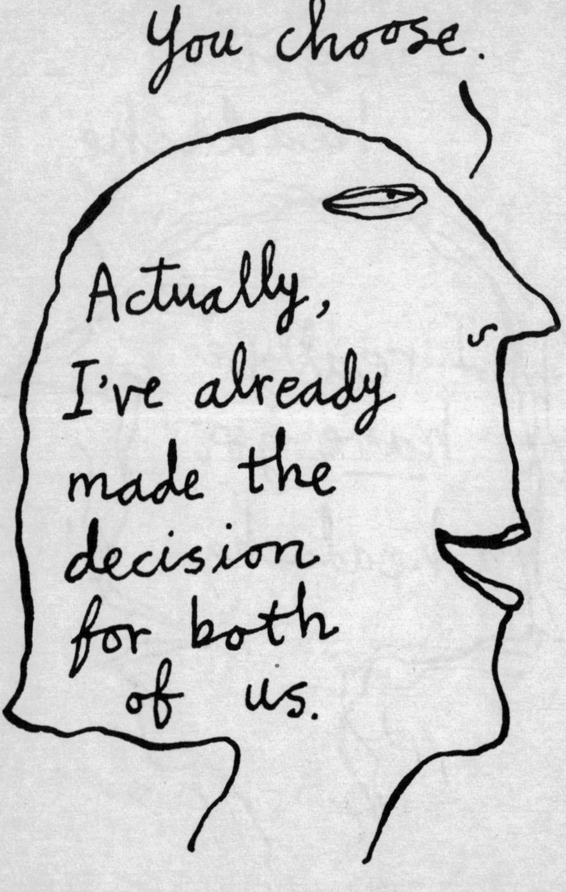
You choose.
Actually, I've already made the decision for both of us.

I've got PMT.
I'm going to disagree with whatever you say and blame it on my hormones.

When we're married I'll...
Live happily ever after?
...make Some changes round here!

After we're married...
I can pass wind and stop bothering to shave my legs.

A THOUGHT TOO
EMBARRASSING TO
SPEAK ALOUD:

I LIKE
being a
house wife.

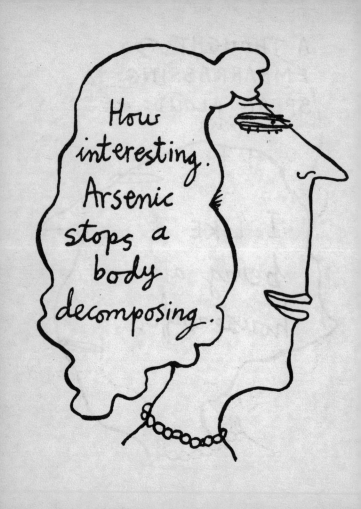

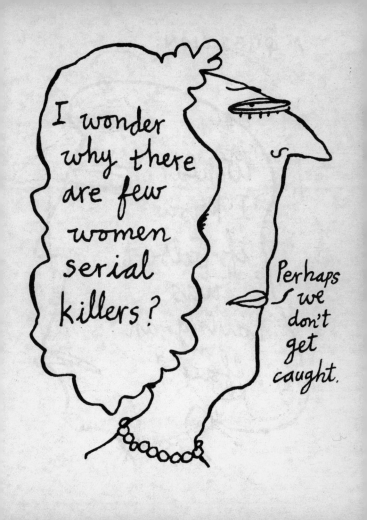

# SOME OBSERVATIONS LEADING TO ONLY ONE CONCLUSION:

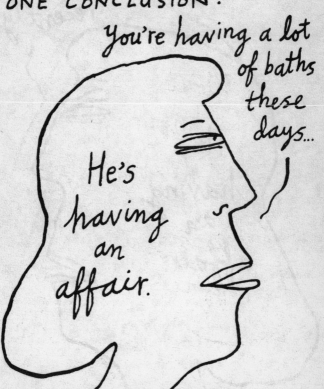

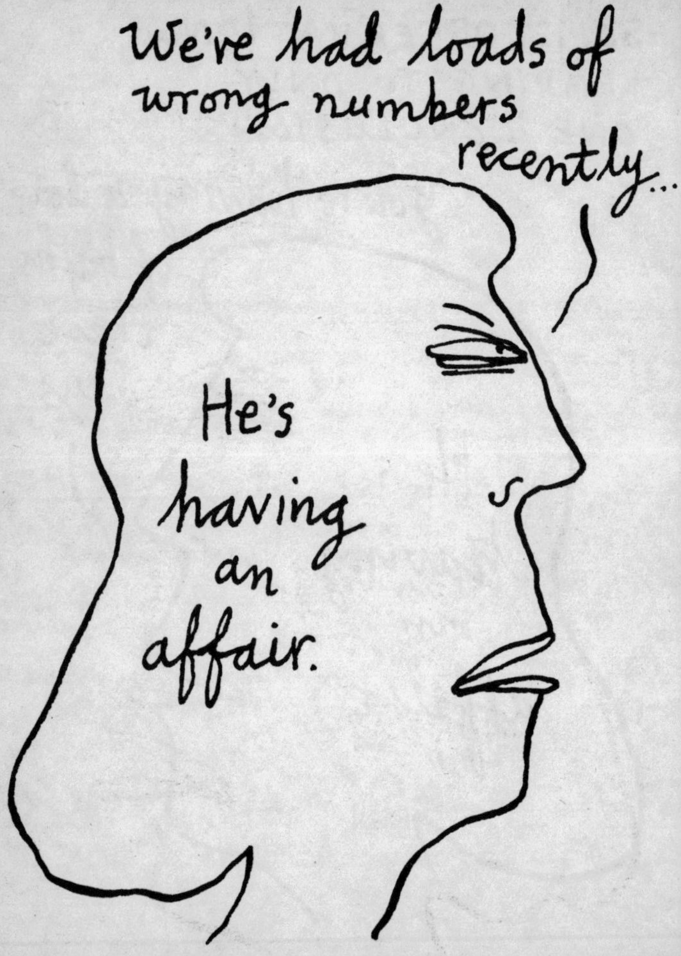
We're had loads of wrong numbers recently...
He's having an affair.

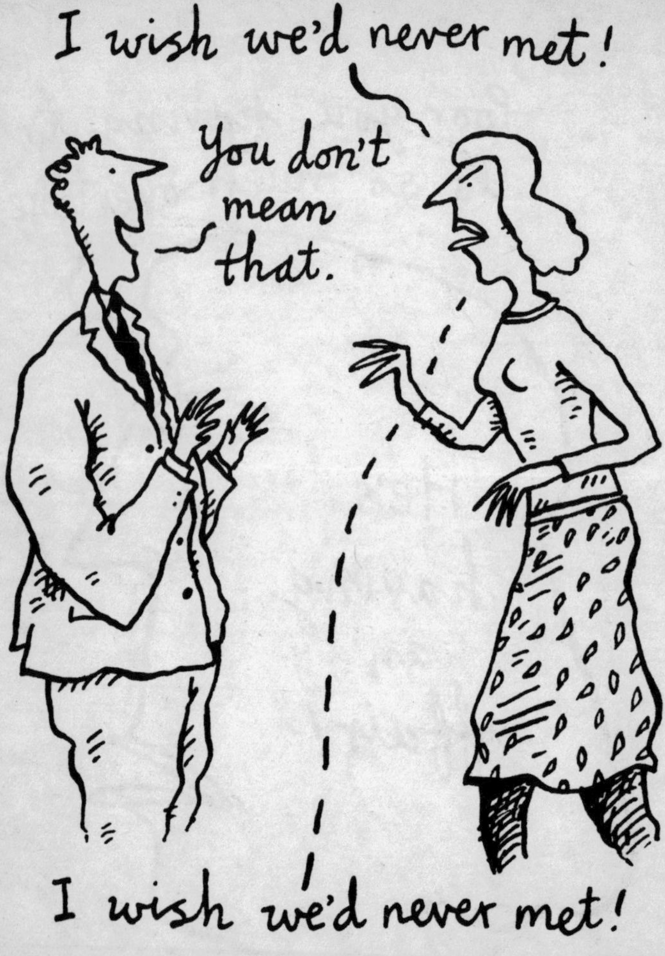
I wish we'd never met!
You don't mean that.
I wish we'd never met!

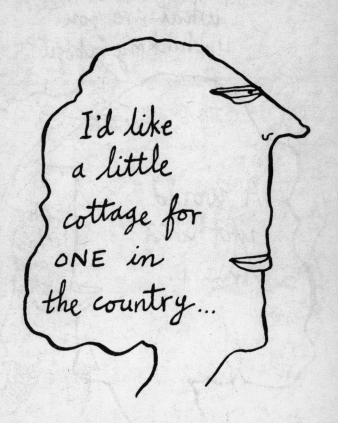

What are you thinking about?
A world without men.
Oh... this and that.

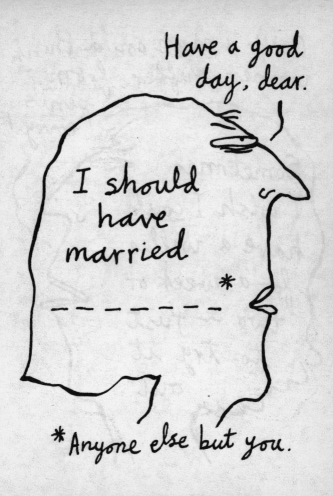

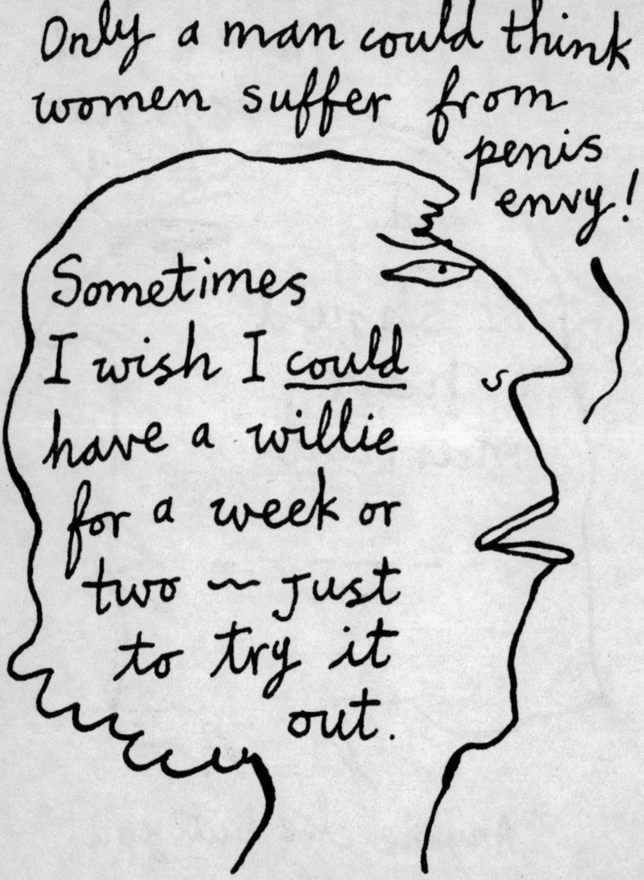
Only a man could think women suffer from penis envy!
Sometimes I wish I could have a willie for a week or two ~ just to try it out.

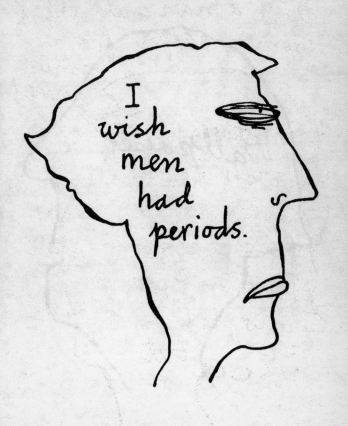

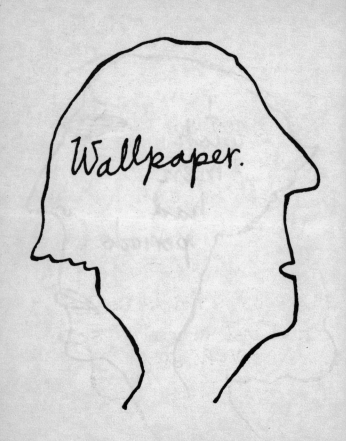

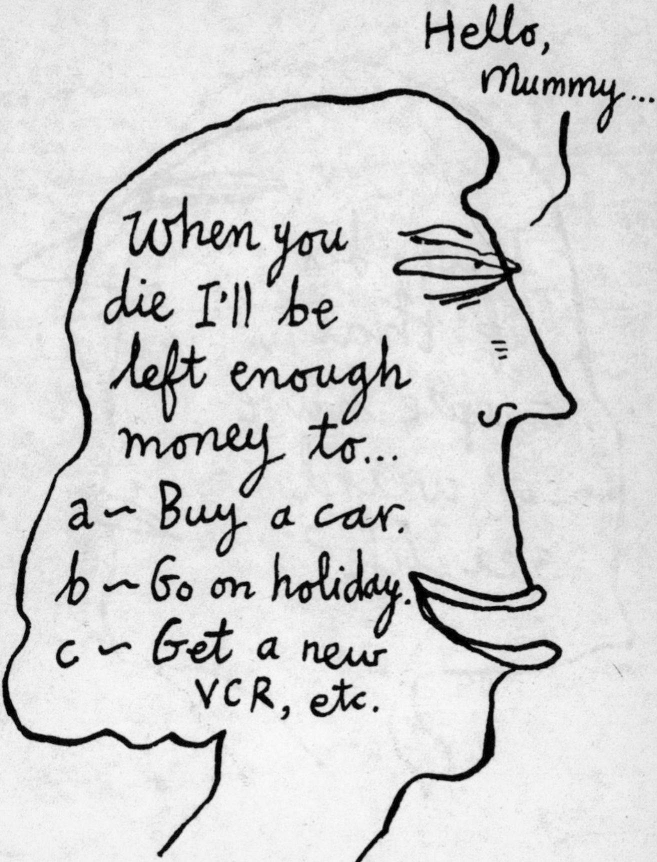
Hello, Mummy...
When you die I'll be left enough money to...
a - Buy a car.
b - Go on holiday.
c - Get a new VCR, etc.

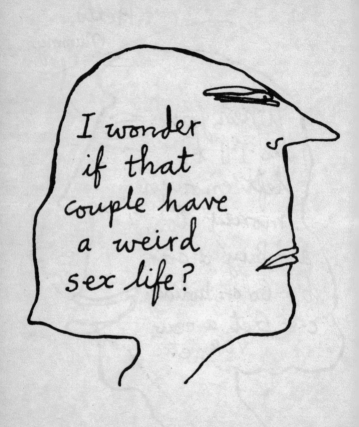

He's much older than her... I expect they're having an affair.

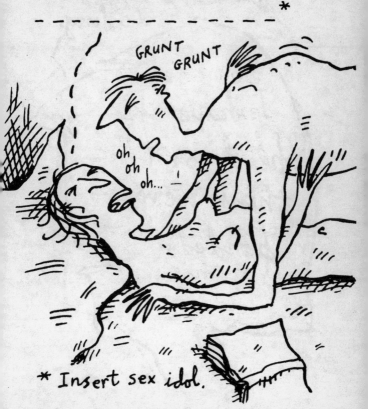

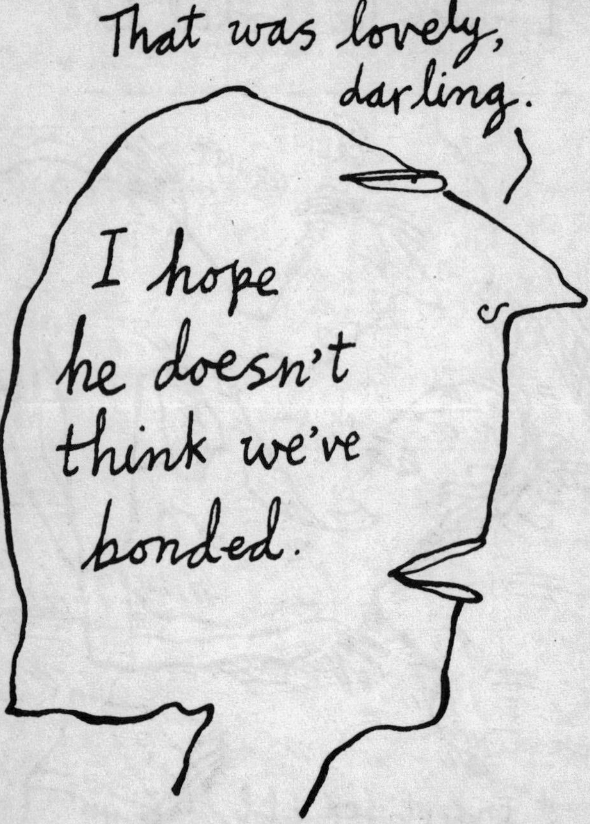
That was lovely, darling.
I hope he doesn't think we've bonded.

I wish
the children
fighting and
being horrible
weren't mine...

And that
mine were
the ones
doing the
colouring-in.

Jim's a few hours late home - I hope he's okay...
Maybe he's been killed by a maniac on the street. That would get me out of this relationship and solve my money worries...

W/up liquid.    Persil/Cond

CHOC!    toilet cleaner    Hoover

Sugar    tampons    bird

Bread    nappies    Bath sponge    cat

butter    flour.

veg:
carrots, peas
potatoes/new
leeks
tomatoes
lettuce
S. onions
cucumber

crisps    (cat
cereals
baby food

arsenic
sharp knives
polythene sheeting.
spade

itiner.
bags

seed

food

litter?)
CHAMPAGNE!!
chocolate.

N.B.
recycle
- newspapers
- jars
- tins etc.
- ~~husband~~.

→ N.B. - Grass seed &
assorted plants.

MAKE ~~XXXX~~ *
* HAIR APPOINTMENT!

Get HOLIDAY BROCHURES!!

new suite.     - passport.
               - ~~travellers'~~
fast car.              cheques
clothes / suitcase(s)
bikini         toothbrush.

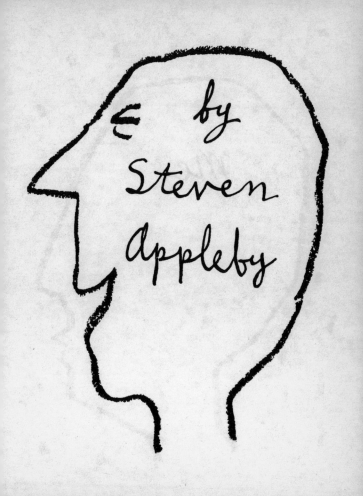

by
Steven
Appleby

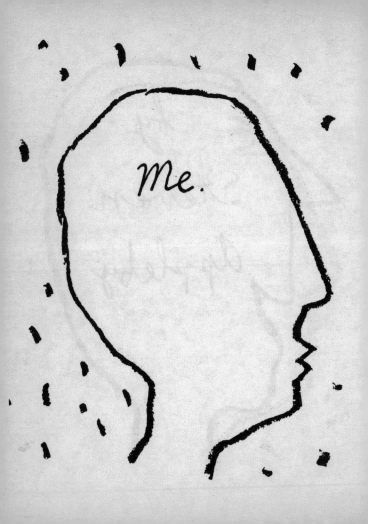

AGE 20

AGE 25

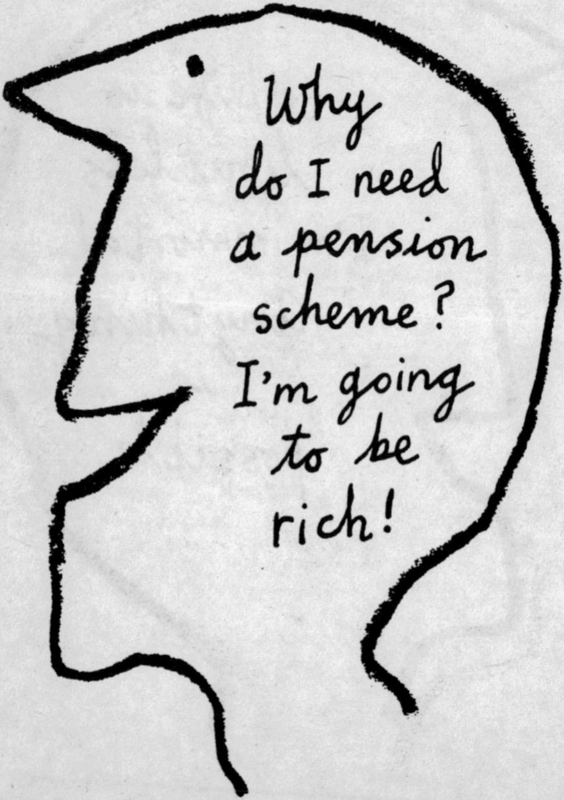

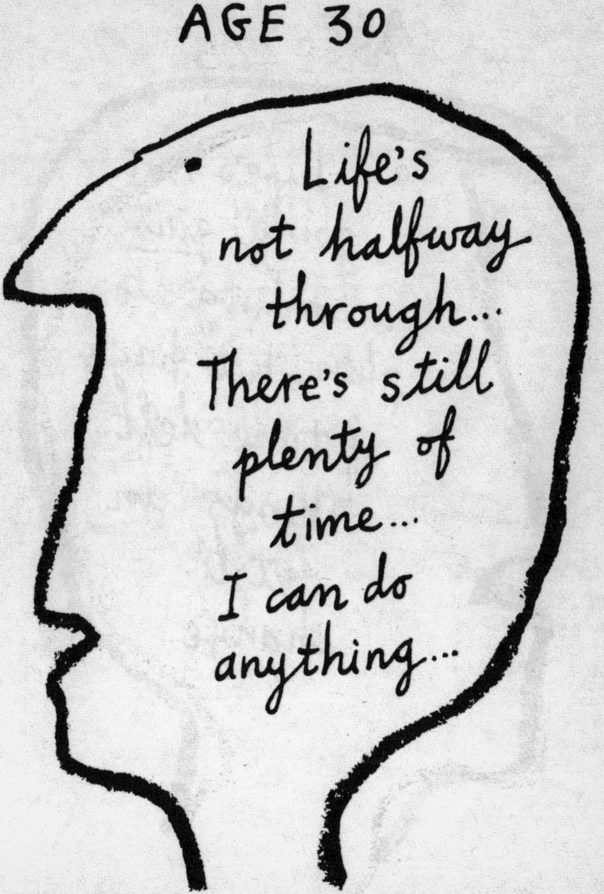
AGE 30
Life's not halfway through... There's still plenty of time... I can do anything...

AGE 40

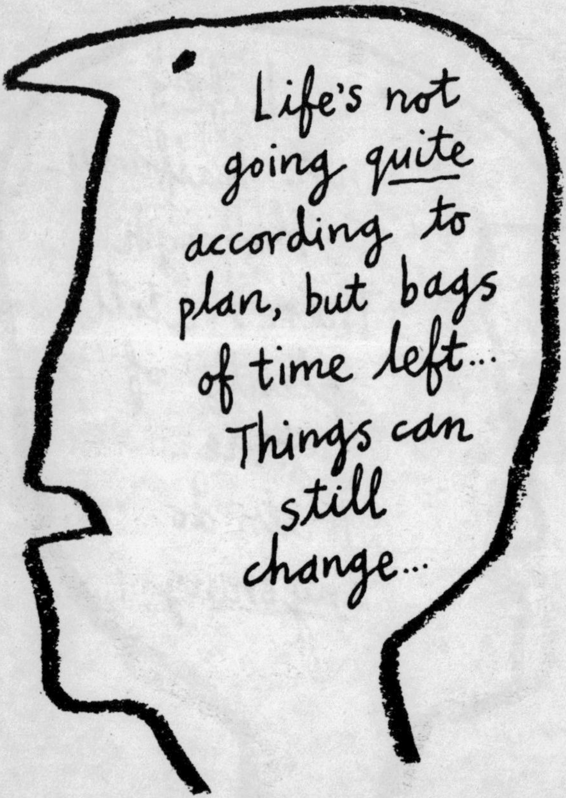
Life's not going quite according to plan, but bags of time left... Things can still change...

AGE 50

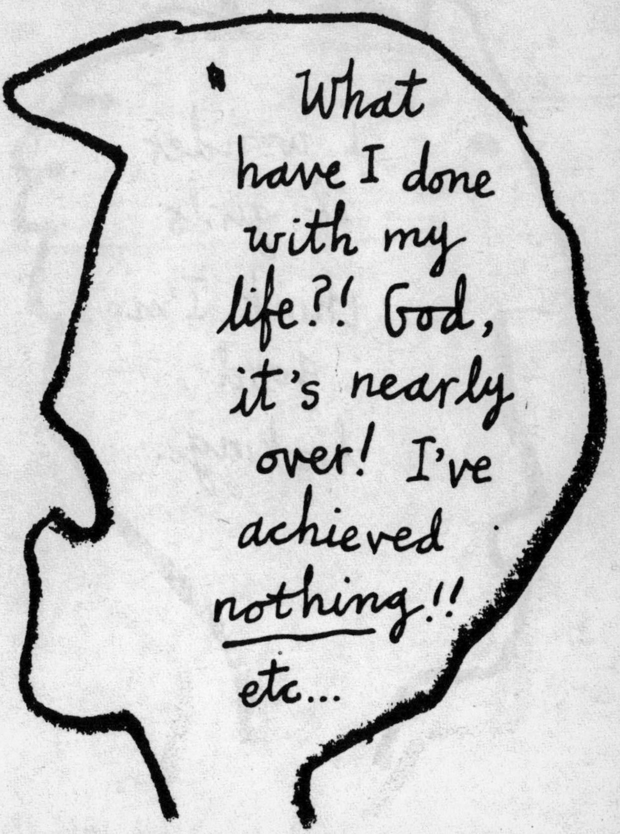
What have I done with my life?! God, it's nearly over! I've achieved nothing!! etc...

I wonder
if girls
think I'm
good-
looking...

Oh how dreadful...
Poor, poor you...
I'm saying that so you'll think I'm a nice person.

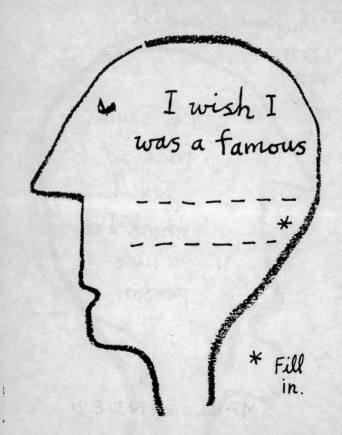

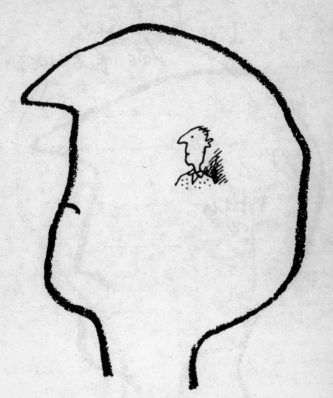

SMALL-MINDED

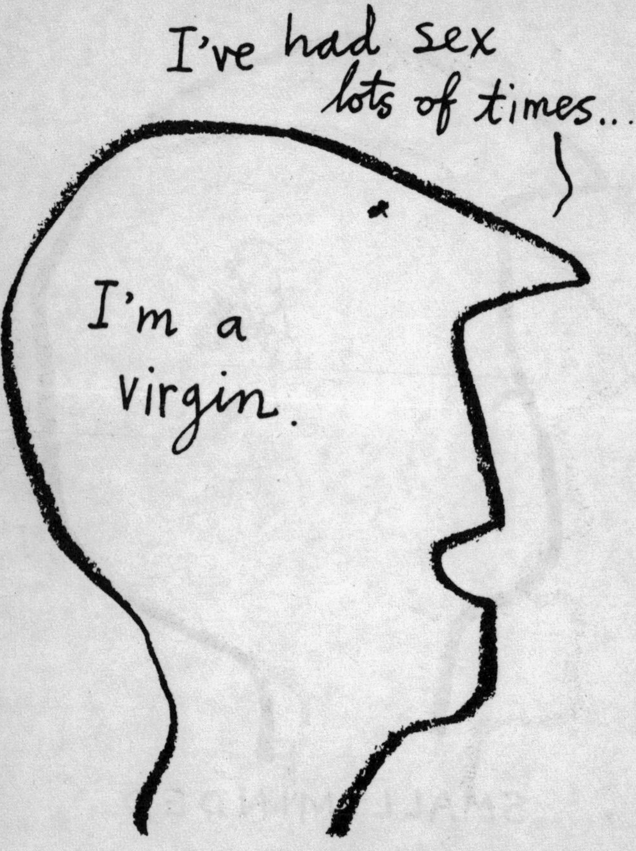
I've had sex lots of times...
I'm a virgin.

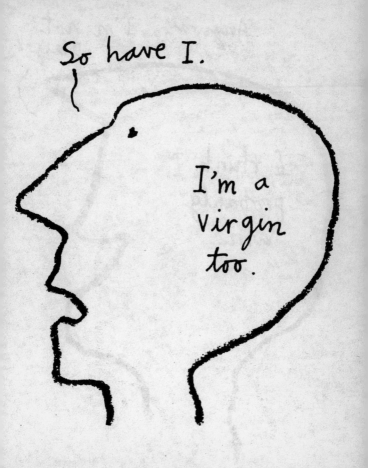

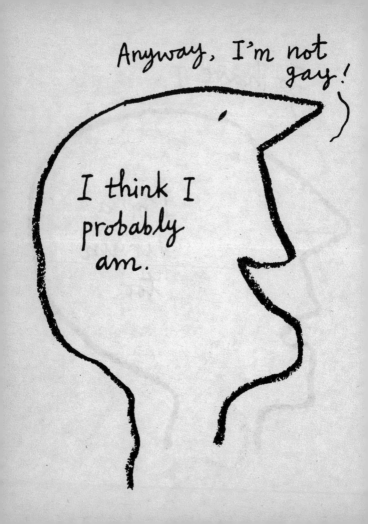

Ho ho... me neither. Ugh!
Except for that time with John. And Stewart... And...

THOUGHTS TOO
EMBARRASSING TO
VOICE ALOUD:

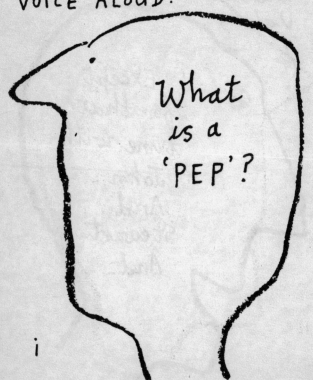

What
is a
'PEP'?

i

Is it
FA cup
final day?
Which
teams are
playing?

ii

Where, exactly, is the clitoris and what does it look like?

iii

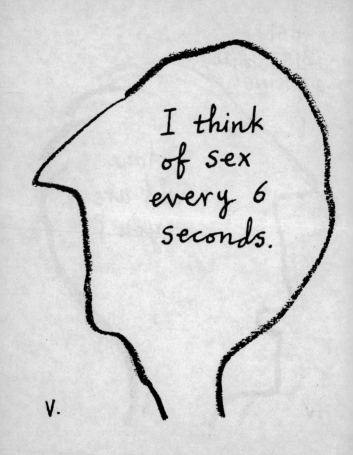

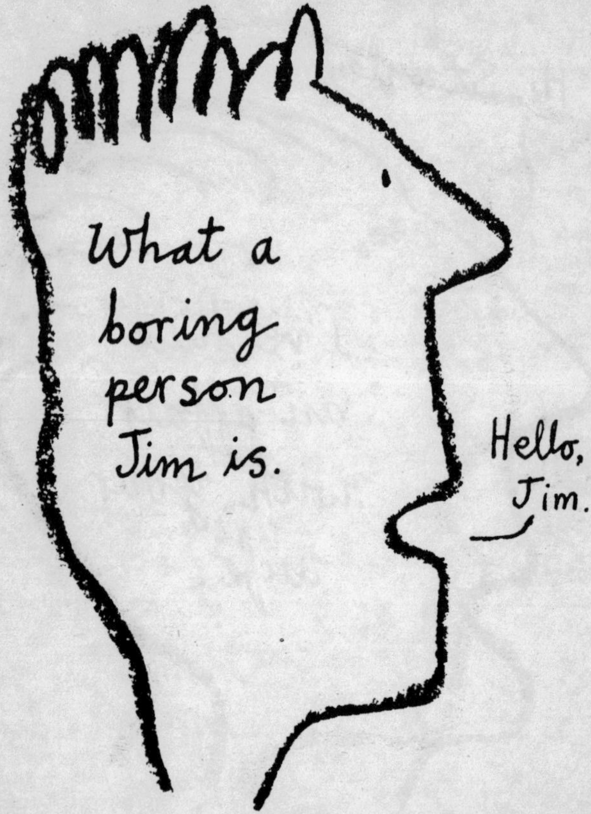
What a boring person Jim is.
Hello, Jim.

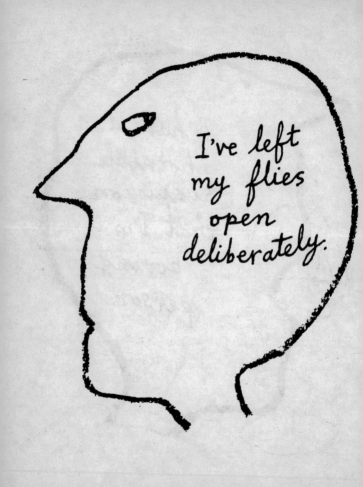

Do you love me?
Yes.
No... Maybe... Don't know... Perhaps... But I do want to have sex with you.

Do you really?
Of course...
not.
But I don't want to hurt your feelings.

Nosepicking time!
Now that we're married I don't need to try anymore.

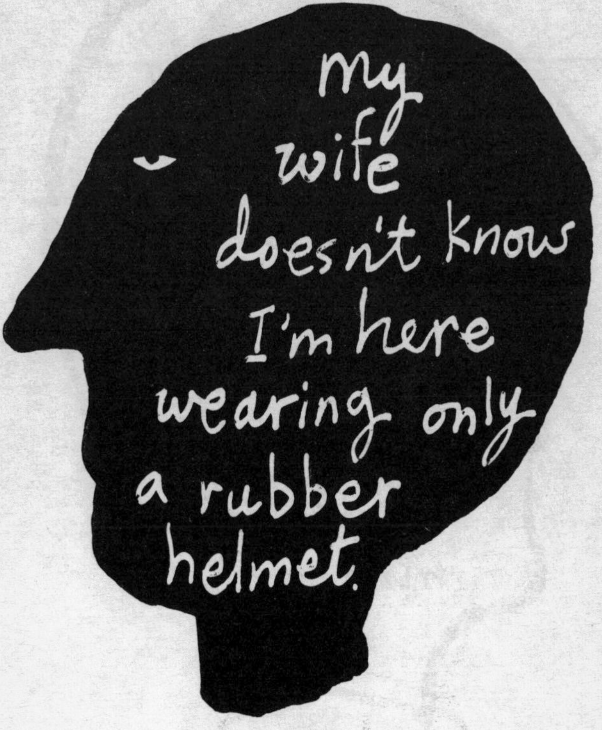
my
wife
doesn't know
I'm here
wearing only
a rubber
helmet.

Why do I feel attracted to other women when I'm happily married?

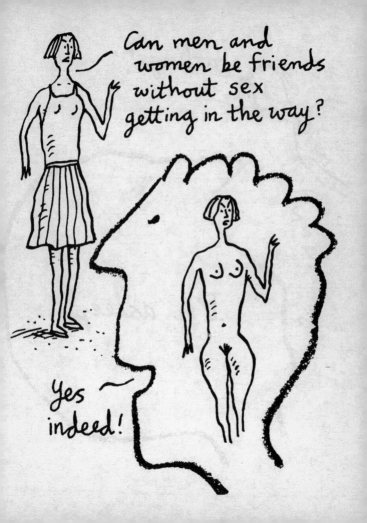

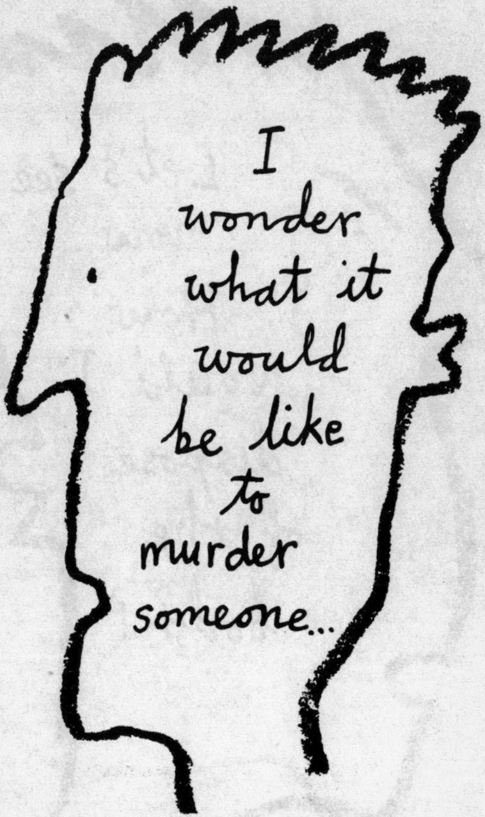
I wonder what it would be like to murder someone...

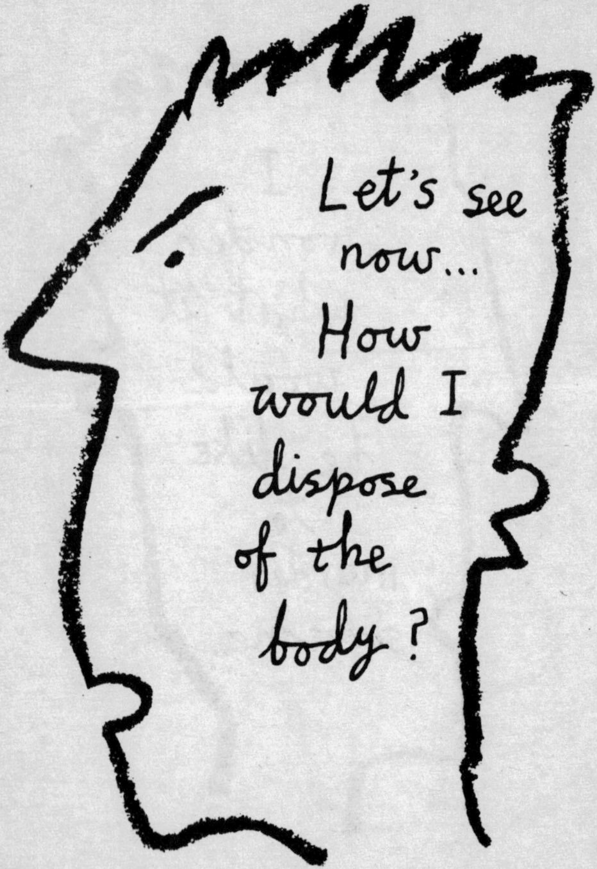
Let's see now... How would I dispose of the body?

I wonder
if other
people
think the
same things
I do?...

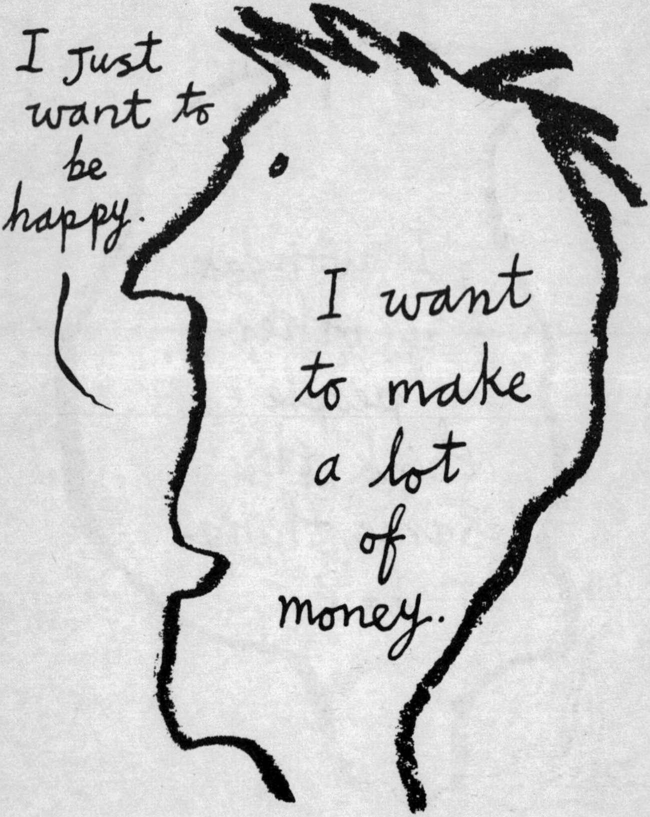
I just want to be happy.
I want to make a lot of money.

The lawnmower and other household items have become indifferent to me.

YAWN...

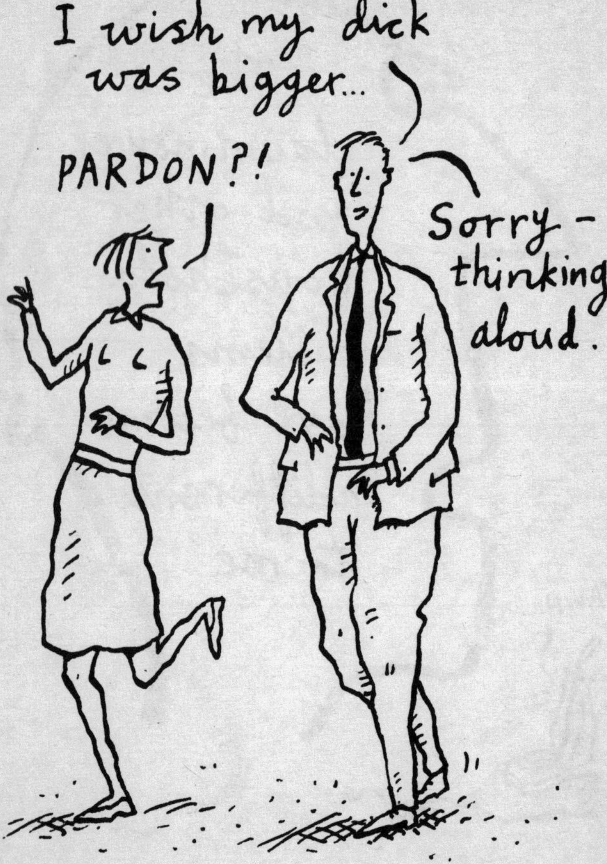
I wish my dick was bigger...
PARDON?!
Sorry - thinking aloud.

Of course, it's well known that women suffer from penis envy.

They wouldn't envy mine if they knew how small it is.

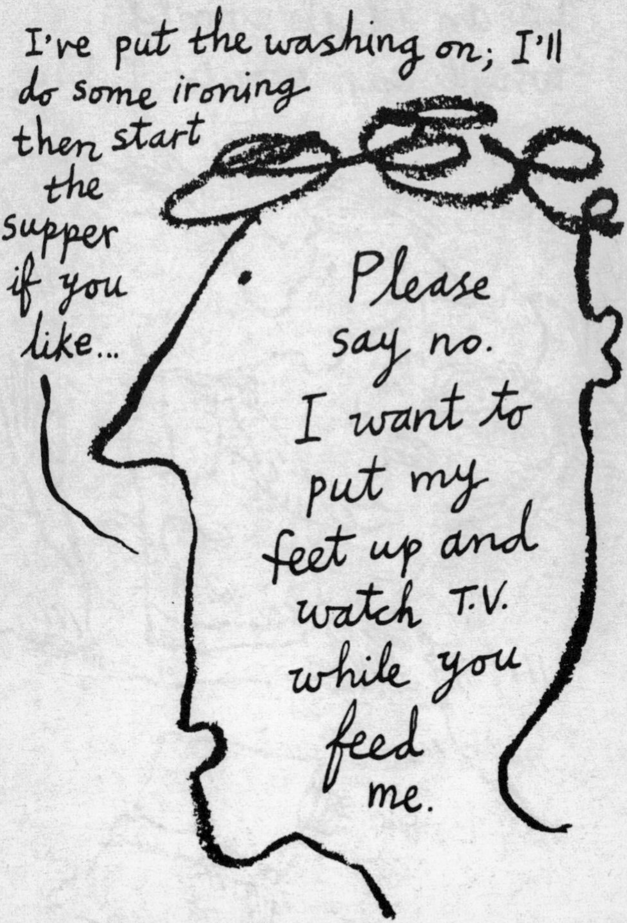
I've put the washing on; I'll do some ironing then start the supper if you like...
Please say no. I want to put my feet up and watch T.V. while you feed me.

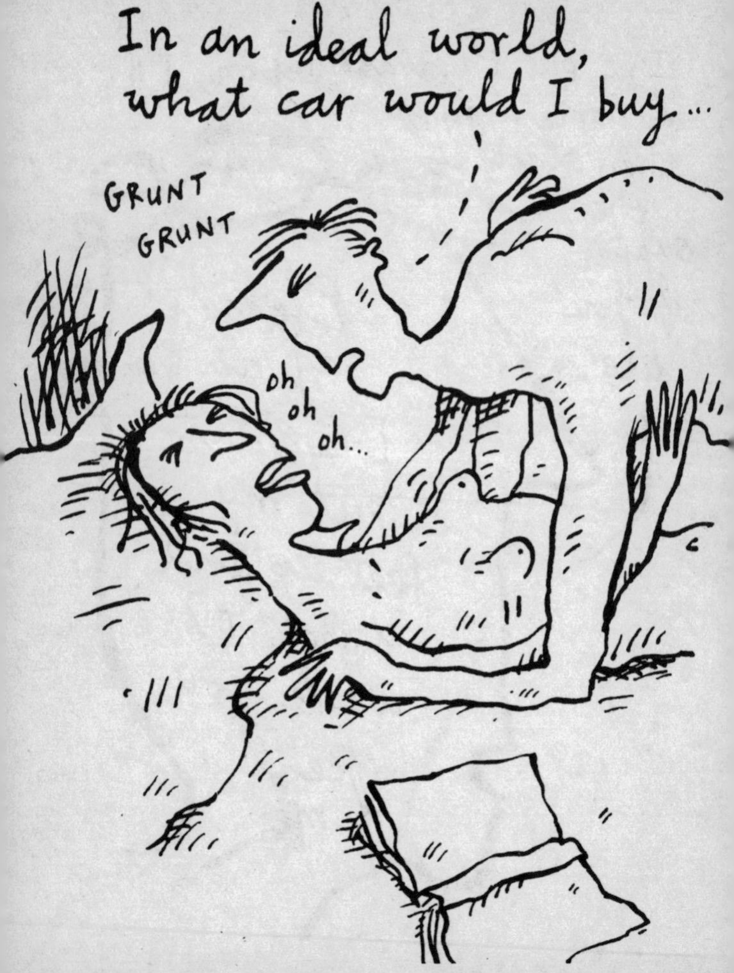
In an ideal world,
what car would I buy...
GRUNT
GRUNT
oh
oh
oh...

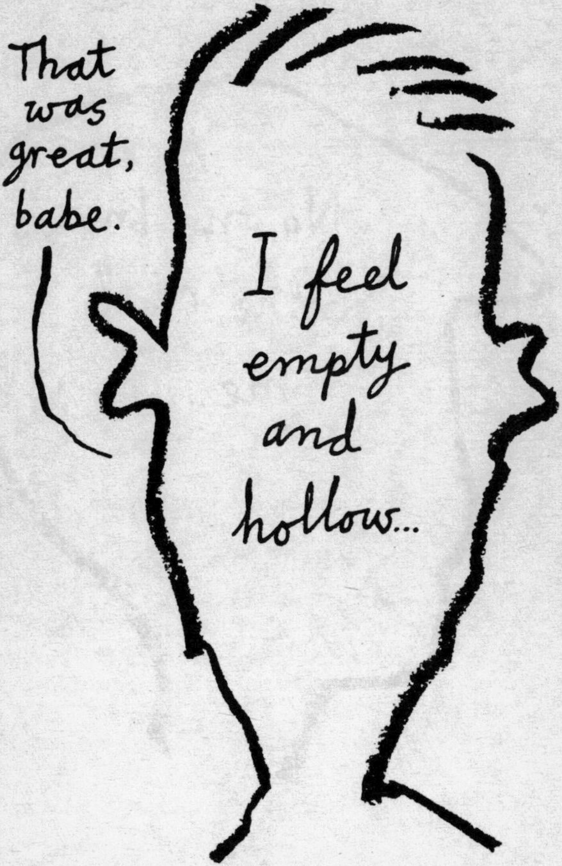
That was great, babe.
I feel empty and hollow...

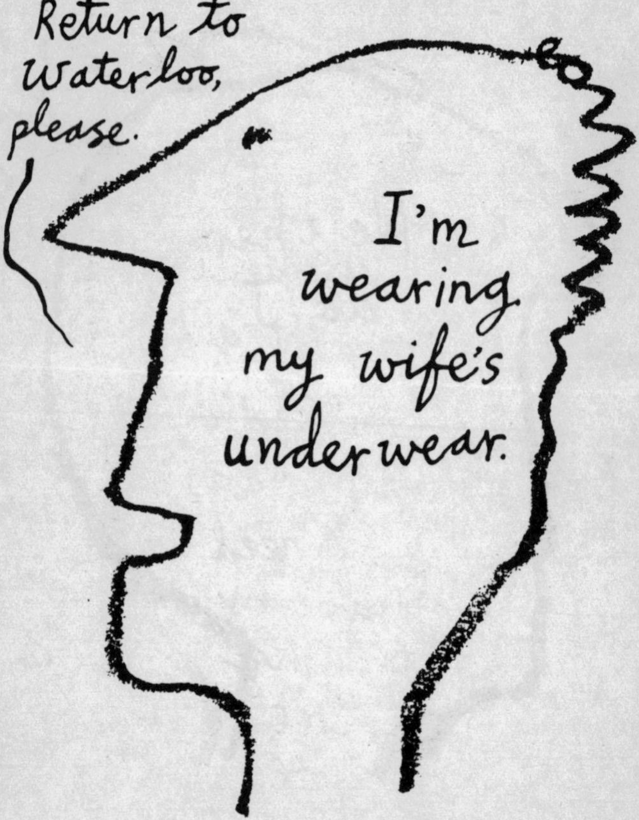
Return to Waterloo, please.
I'm wearing my wife's underwear.

I
hope I
don't get
knocked down
by a car
and need to
have my
clothing
cut
off...

My family are the most important thing in my life.
The children? My wife looks after them.

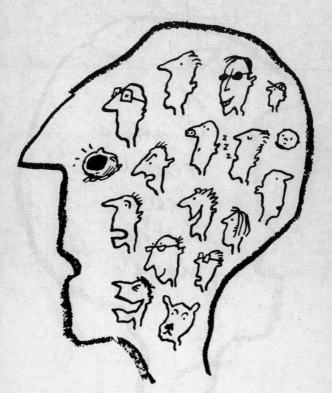

MULTIPLE PERSONALITY

I am a
creature
from
another
planet.

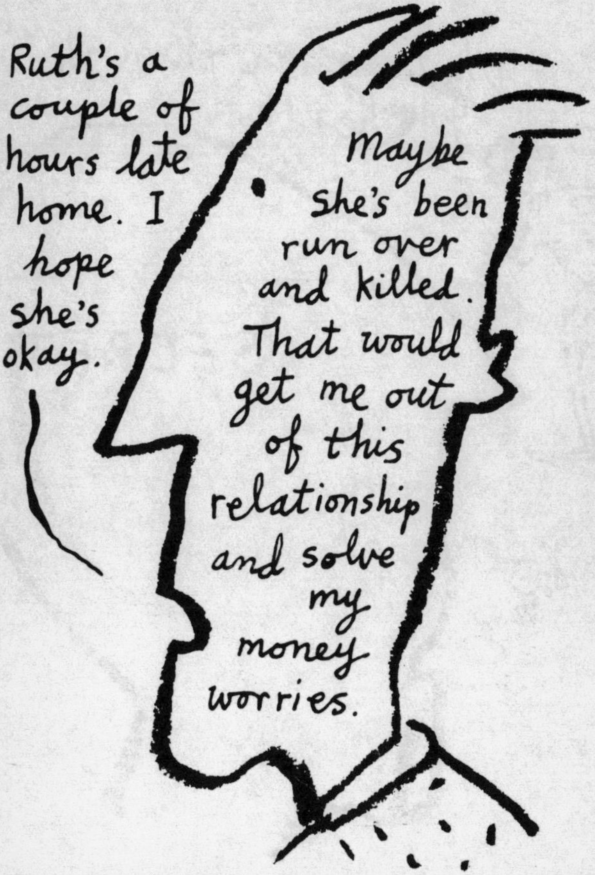
Ruth's a couple of hours late home. I hope she's okay.
Maybe she's been run over and killed. That would get me out of this relationship and solve my money worries.

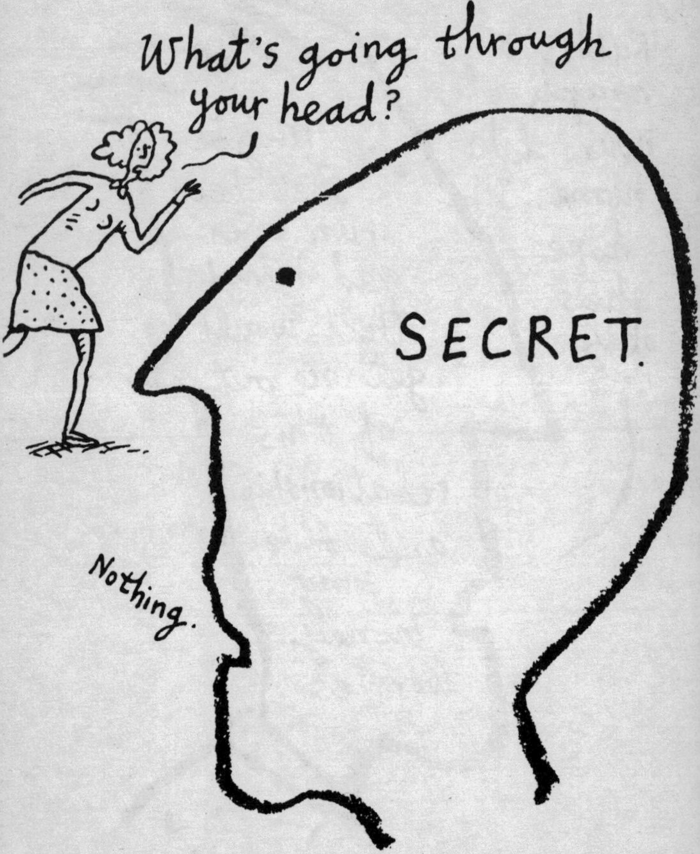
What's going through your head?
SECRET.
Nothing.

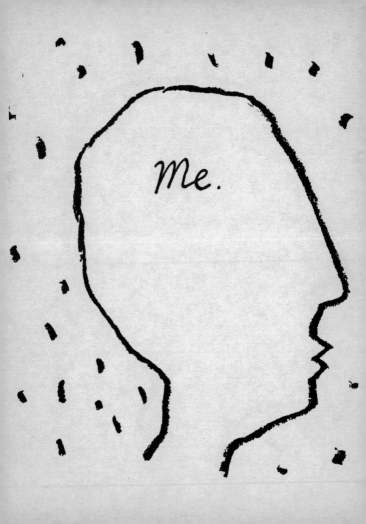